THE SILVEY-JEX PARTNERSHIP

DALESMAN

Dalesman Publishing Company
Stable Courtyard, Broughton Hall, Skipton, North Yorkshire BD23 3AE

First Edition 1996

A British Library Cataloguing in Publication record is available for this book

ISBN 185568 104 8

Printed by The Amadeus Press Ltd, Huddersfield

THE SILVEY-JEX PARTNERSHIP

WOW! GREAT THERMALS! FROM THE LAKE DISTRICT TO ER....WHEREVER THIS IS.

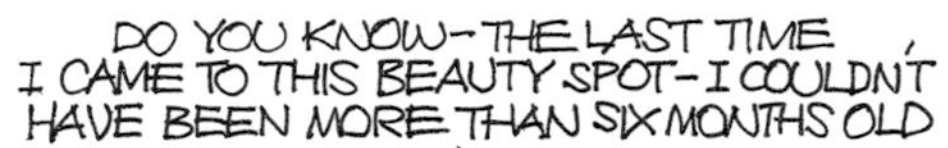
DO YOU KNOW - THE LAST TIME I CAME TO THIS BEAUTY SPOT - I COULDN'T HAVE BEEN MORE THAN SIX MONTHS OLD

BABY FOOD
BABY FOOD
BABY FOOD
NAPPIES
SJ.

LIKE YOUR HOME COMFORTS THEN MISSUS?

. . . BUT THE BROCHURE SAID "IDEAL FOR CLUBS"

LAZY BLIGHTER

WILL... YOU... GET... OFF!!!

. . . I WANT TO MAKE A NICE EARLY START IN THE MORNING

BUT DON'T YOU FEEL JUST THE TINIEST BIT GUILTY?
SJ.

HMM...LOOKS LIKE A TRICKY BIT COMING UP ROGER !

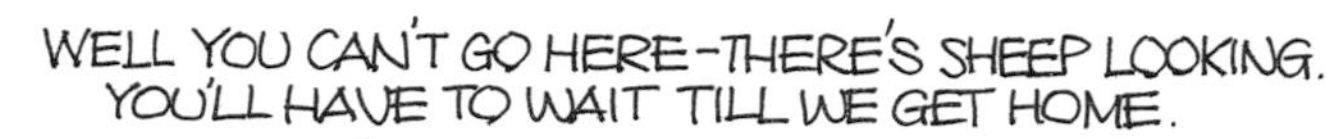
WELL YOU CAN'T GO HERE–THERE'S SHEEP LOOKING.
YOU'LL HAVE TO WAIT TILL WE GET HOME.

DAFT MODERN INVENTIONS
- WHAT'S WRONG WITH THE
OLD FLAT CAP?
SJ.

SLURRY
KEEP OFF

WHY DO YOU ALWAYS DRAG ME ALONG ON YOUR WALKING HOLIDAYS?

...WELL WE'VE TREKKED FOR MILES AND I HAVEN'T SEEN A PONY ALL DAY

SJ.

WON'T GIVE UP YOUR DAD ... WILL HE ?

POT HOLERS AT WORK
ANTS NEST
SJ.

EVERYTHING LOOKS SO SMALL FROM UP HERE DOESN'T IT?
MAP OF THE FELLS

THIS WAY EVERYBODY...

JUST COULDN'T WAKE THE WIFE UP THIS MORNING

THE WEST SURREY SYNCHRONIZED WALKING CLUB

DAILY NEWS
SJ.

SUDDENLY I'VE GONE OFF THE IDEA OF PONY TREKKING
SJ.

AAAH LOOK.... A BUNNY RABBIT

YOU TEAR THAT PICNIC CLOTH AND THERE'LL BE TROUBLE

HMMM NICE—BUT NOT QUITE THE WALKING SHOES I HAD IN MIND

OH LOOK WHAT DADDY'S BROUGHT ALONG...
NOW IF IT RAINS A LOT TONIGHT WE'LL ALL BE SAFE

GOOD FUN ISN'T IT?

SEE THE BABY LAMBS AT PLAY

ARE YOU GOING TO BE LONG "MR. LEAVE IT TO ME I KNOW WHAT I'M DOING"?

CAMPSITE
FULL
BIG TOP
SJ.

VIRTUAL REALITY HELMET
FELL RUNNING
Absailing
ROCK CLIMBING
POT HOLING

YOU ASK IT WHERE WE ARE

WHAT KEPT YOU ?

LOVERS'
LEAP

WILL YOU STOP YOUR SHOUTING WOMAN – YOU'LL FRIGHTEN THE FISH

WE'RE GOING ROUND IN CIRCLES IF YOU ASK ME

BUT WHAT'S WRONG WITH A SOUVENIR ASHTRAY OR SOMETHING?

SORRY.... THERE WAS A QUEUE IN THE LADIES

THERE WE ARE–YOUR VERY OWN TENT. NIP OUT THE BACK AND TAKE A LOOK AT THE VIEW
SJ.

THIS IS THE LIFE EH BERT ?

IT'S THAT STUPID TEDDY BEAR SHOULDER BAG THEY'RE AFTER

ALRIGHT, ALRIGHT... SO IT'S DEEPER THAN IT LOOKS

BEWARE
OF
FALLING
ROCKS
SJ.

PLEASE DO NOT FEED THE ALLIGATORS

NOW SOME OF US ARE BORN POT-HOLERS – SOME ARE NOT, MR WILKINSON

GOOD TO SEE THE OLD METHODS HAVEN'T DIED OUT
SJ.

S.J.

I SEE THE CORN IS AS HIGH AS AN ELEPHANT'S EYE....

OOH LOOK.... A HEDGEHOG

HOME MADE
HONEY

CAREFUL HERE LADS... THIS CAVES GOT A PARTICULARLY BAD REPUTATION

THE FUTURE
THE PAST
MAP
SJ.

S.J.

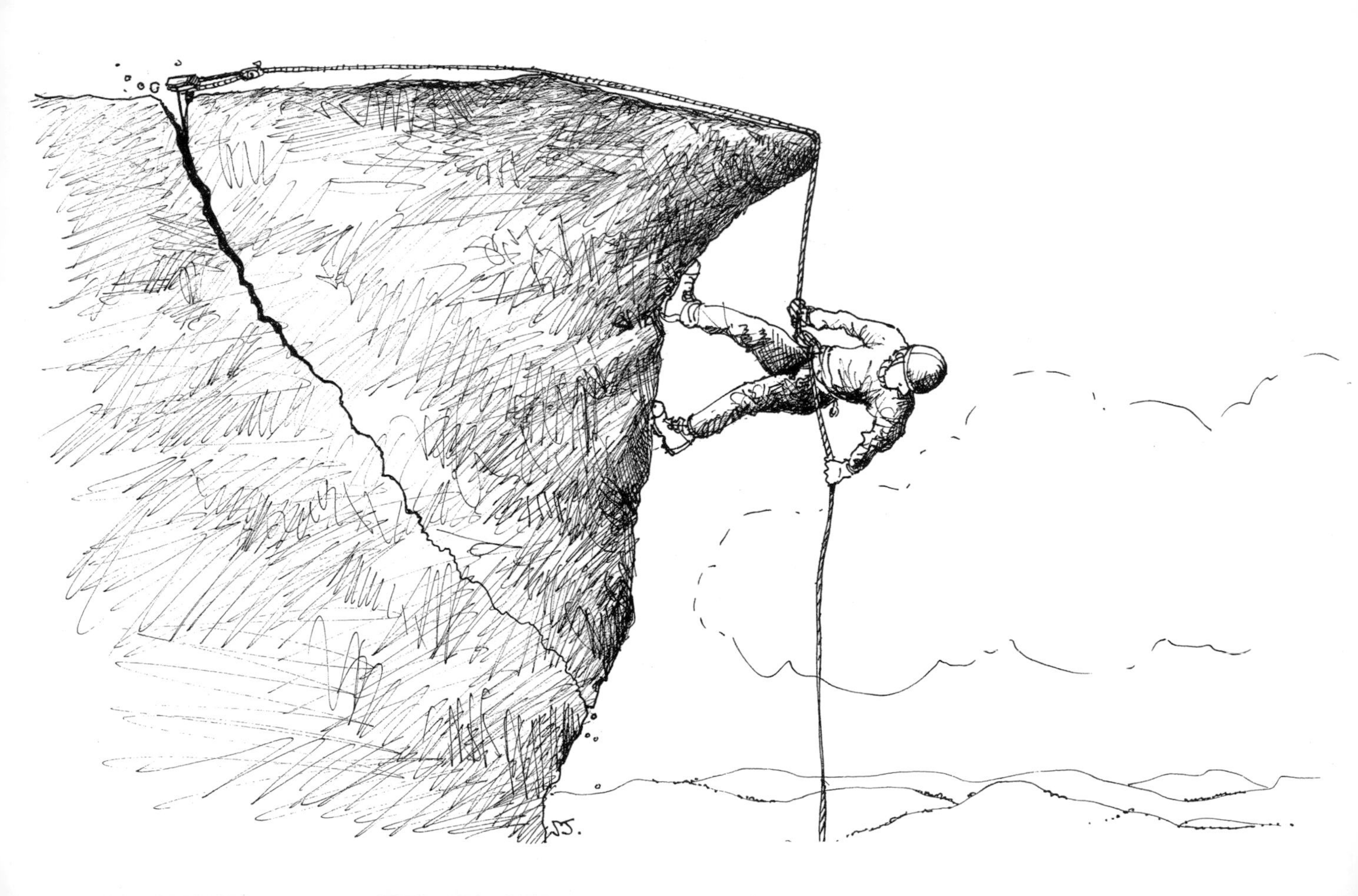
WJ.

HERE THEY COME DORIS-
BANG ON TIME
BLESS 'EM
NEXT FLY PAST 2·30 p.m.
BIRD WATCHERS WEEKLY

BE CAREFUL – SOME OF THESE ROCKS ARE A BIT SLIPPERY

FORGET IT... YOU'RE NOT GETTING ME DOWN THERE!

DIDN'T I SAY THE LAST BIT WAS EASY ?

WELL I THINK YOU'RE DELIBERATELY LOOKING FOR TROUBLE
BED & BREAKFAST
XXX
S.J.

DON'T PANIC ELIZABETH... I'VE GOT YOUR HANDBAG

UMM... I CAN EXPLAIN!

TO BE HONEST I HAVEN'T BEEN ANYWHERE...IT'S A SECONDHAND BACKPACK

DON'T LOOK NOW REG, BUT YOUR BAIT IS GETTING AWAY

XXX

WELL ... I'VE GOT TO ADMIRE YOUR STYLE
SJ.

THERE THEY GO... UP TO THE SUMMER PASTURES

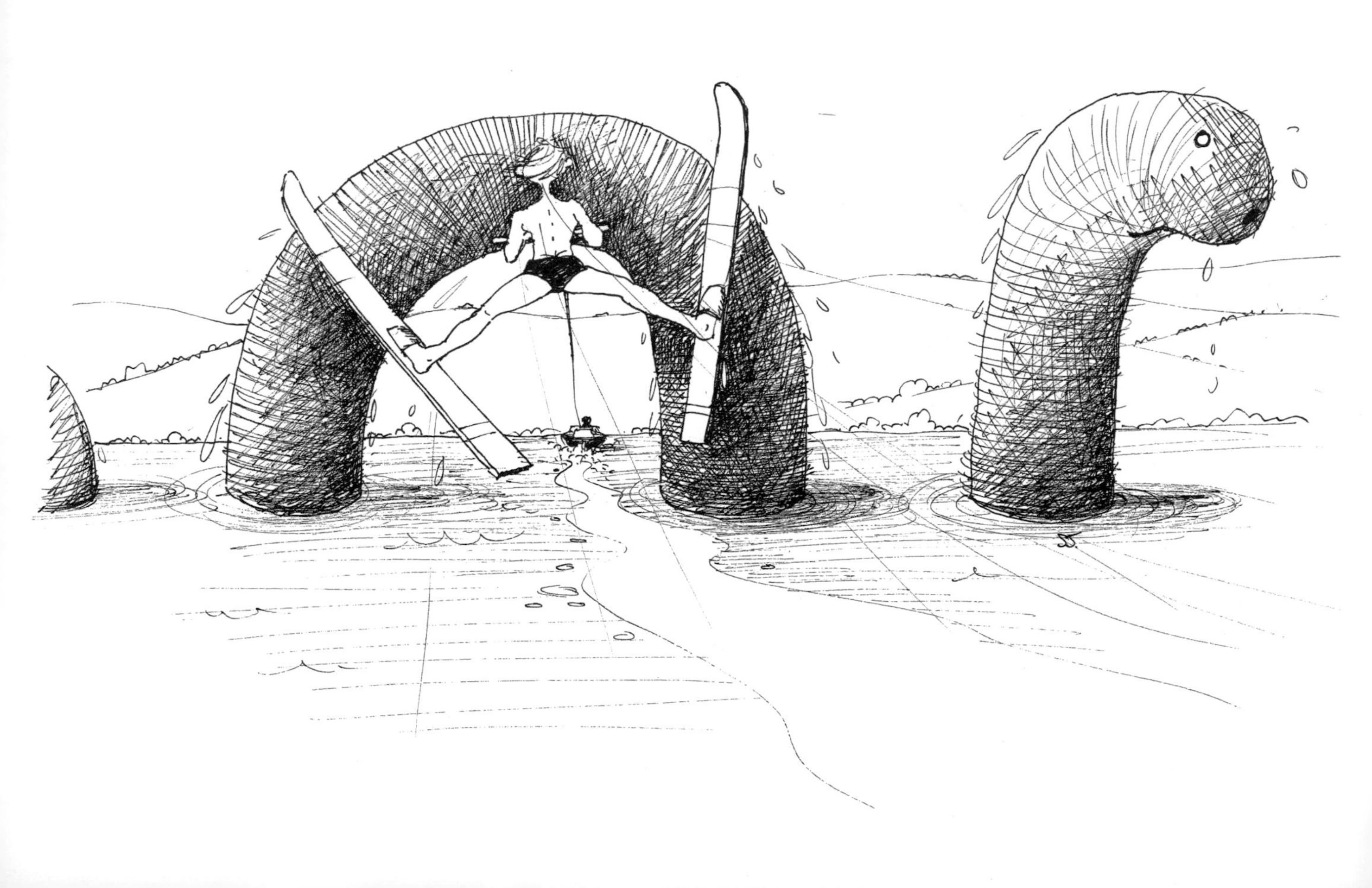

DAMN IT MARTHA – I'LL TELL YOU WHEN TO JETTISON BALLAST

... OKAY, IF THAT'S A HANG GLIDER – WHERE'S THE TENT ?

WHAT THE DEVIL
WAS THAT?

COME AND LOOK AT THIS

JUST
MARRIED
BEAN

CYCLE HIRE
EXPLORE THE DALES THE HARD WAY

THERE'S A REALLY SECLUDED SPOT ALONG HERE...
NOBODY WOULD KNOW YOU WERE THERE

JUST LIKE A
PATCHWORK QUILT
ISN'T IT?
SJ.

WE SHOULD HAVE
BROUGHT MOTHER
SHOULD'NT WE?
YES

I THINK YOU'VE VIOLATED HIS SACRED BURIAL GROUND

I USUALLY GET SOMEBODY TO DO THE FELL RUNNING FOR ME